My life as a dog

John and Marilyn Talbot

Illustrated by Fred Apps

Nelson

Contents

Chapter I Slow down!

My name is Max.
Yes, I am a dog.
I live in Wellington Square with Rocky and his Mum.
They look after me very well.
Rocky trained me, you know.
When I was a young dog he trained me to
'come here', to 'stay' and to 'sit'.
Then he trained me to roll over.
This was fun because Rocky gave me some
dog biscuits every time I did it right.
He also trained me to do other tricks.

The really difficult one to learn was to
bark at a burglar.
At first I got it all wrong.
I would bark at anyone who came to the house, like
the milkman and Rocky's friends.
What does a burglar look like?
I don't know!

Every day Rocky takes me for a walk.
I just love walking around Wellington Square.
The gate to the little park is right across the
road from our house, so we always go there first.
When I have had my tea I know it's time for my walk.
Sometimes Rocky makes me wait.
He is watching TV and has forgotten all about me.
'Come on Rocky. It's time for my walk,' I bark.
'Yes, I'm coming,' says Rocky, but he still makes
me wait.
So, I go and get my lead.
That's one of my own tricks.
I try rattling it in front of him.
'Come on, Rocky. Come on!'
'Is it time for your walk, Max?' says Rocky.
At last he puts on my lead, and off we go.

I love the park.
The smell and the noises are so exciting.
But I really love the trees.
All dogs love trees.
'Slow down, Max!'
I can hear Rocky calling me.
He's not in a hurry to get there, but I am!
It's true, I don't like to be on a lead, but I don't
chase cats any more.
You may remember the day I chased Mrs Valentine's
cat, Sing-sing, up a tree.
Really it was Sing-sing who started that.
She hissed at me, so there!

So many things have happened to me.
Once I got caught in a fox trap.
Then there was the day I followed Rocky to school.
But the most dangerous thing that ever happened to me took place right here in Wellington Square.
I'll tell you what happened.

Chapter 2 Danger! Keep Out!

It was last summer.
We were in the park together.
Rocky threw a stick for me to bring back to him.
He threw it a long way. It went right over a new
fence, one I had never seen before.
The fence had a new sign on it which said,
'Danger! Keep Out!'
But dogs can't read, so I jumped over the
fence anyway.
Did I get a surprise!
On the other side of the fence, waiting for me was
a hole. A big hole!
I heard Rocky shout, 'No, Max! No!'
But it was too late.

I couldn't stop. I was going too quickly.
I fell right down the hole.
I went down and down.
It got darker and darker.
I just kept going.
Let me tell you, I thought it would never end.
But at last it did, and with a very hard bump!
It took me a few minutes to sort out what had happened.
The first thing I saw was a little bit of daylight at the top of the hole.
Then I heard Rocky calling to me.
He sounded strange and far away.
'Max, Max, are you OK?'
'Get me out!' I barked. 'Get me out!'
I soon found out that this was not going to be easy.
Then I heard another one of my friends.
It was Fred.
'He sounds all right,' he said.
But I wasn't all right. I had hurt my back leg.
I was sure it was broken. I tried to tell them.
'Woof, woof, woof! Woof!'
But I don't think they understood.

'How can we get him out?'
I heard Rocky ask.
'I'll go and call the fire brigade,'
said Fred.
'Don't worry, Max.
We will soon have you out, boy,'
Rocky called down to me.
Then I heard Rocky's Mum.
She sounded cross with Rocky.
'How did you let this happen?'
she wanted to know.
Then I heard other people talking.
They all wanted to know what
was going on.
Rocky never stopped
talking to me all the time I
was stuck down that horrible hole.

And then, it started to rain.

It was cold and wet down that hole and my leg hurt.
What had I done to make this happen?
I started to think about it.
I was always getting into trouble.
I remembered the time I ate all the birthday cake at
my party. Rocky and his Mum came in and found me
sitting on the table.
Then there was the time I ran off with Mr Keeping's
bag. I opened it up and let the snake out.
I made a lot of trouble that day.
I remembered how I ran around in the park like a
wild thing. I jumped in the pond and frightened the
birds.
Fred was very angry.
Yes, I have been a very bad dog.
That's why this has happened to me.

But just then I heard Rocky calling again.
'Max, Max, I am going to let down some food on the
end of this line. Here it comes.'
A minute later a plate of lovely food was
dropped down in front of me.
The smell was great!
I was so hungry I ate it in a flash.
It was the best food I had ever eaten.
I felt better.

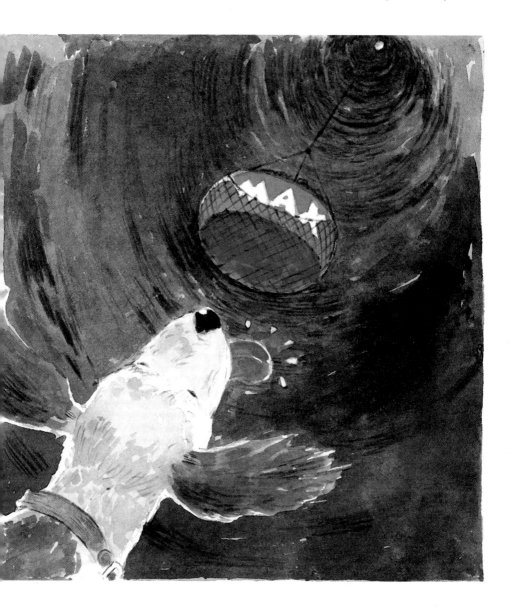

Then it started to get dark.
I was frightened.

I was feeling really sorry for myself when I heard
Rocky talking to me again.
'You are a very good dog, Max,' he said. 'Remember
the time I fell off the swing and had to go to hospital.
You stayed with me all the time until the ambulance
came.'

Then I heard a lady.
'Max, Max. It's me, Mrs Valentine. I'm not cross with
you for chasing Sing-sing up that tree. I remember
how you woke Rocky up when my house was on fire.
Rocky telephoned the fire brigade and the fire was
put out. If it wasn't for you, I might not be here today.
Thank you, Max, and I hope they get you out soon!'

Then I heard someone I knew very well.
It was Mr Patel from the shop in Wellington Square.
'Max, I know I always chase you out of my shop. But
it's not because I don't like you. It's because we don't
let any dogs into our shop.
I hope you get out soon, old boy.
By the way, Jamila sends her love.'

Everyone in Wellington Square was worried about me.
I was starting to get worried too.
Would I ever get out of this hole?

Chapter 3 Stuck in the mud

What was that?

I knew that noise.

It was the siren of the fire engine. It was getting nearer.

When I looked up I could see the flash, flash, flash of its alarm light.

Then I heard Fireman Salter speaking. 'The hole is too small for one of my men to go down on a line,' he said.

'Let me go down,' I heard Rocky say. 'He is my dog after all.'

'I can't let you do that, Rocky,' said Fireman Salter. 'It might be dangerous. You can only try if your Mum says it's all right.'

'Oh please, Mum. Please can I go down,' said Rocky.

At first his Mum didn't want him to go.

But at last she said, 'OK, Rocky. But be very careful.'

Then they all stopped talking.

They were doing something up there but it was too far away for me to see.

Rocky looked down the hole and told me what was happening.

'The firemen are putting up some lifting gear, Max.
They have a long wire. I'm coming down to you on
the wire. Fireman Salter has given me this
helmet with a TV camera on it. Don't be scared,
It's going to be OK.'
But I was scared.
I was scared for me and I was scared for Rocky.
The firemen tied Rocky's legs together and lifted
him over the hole.
Bit by bit they let him down, head first into this
horrible dark hole.
I could hear them shouting a long way away.
'Good luck, Rocky! Good luck!'
I was so pleased with Rocky.
He would soon get me out.
Everyone at the top could see it on a small TV that
the firemen had brought with them.
'So far, so good,' said Fireman Salter.

Half way down there was trouble.
The hole was getting smaller and smaller.
Rocky made himself as thin as he could, but the hole
was still too small for him.
I heard him shout, 'I'm stuck! I'm stuck!'
'OK, Rocky,' said Fireman Salter. 'We will
pull you back out.'
But when they started pulling they found that Rocky
couldn't move.
The wet mud was holding him tightly on every side.
He couldn't go up or down!
'Stop!' he shouted, 'stop!'
The firemen stopped pulling and it all went quiet.

'Rocky, can you hear me?' asked Fireman Salter.
'Yes,' said Rocky, but he sounded frightened.
'What part of you is stuck?' asked Fireman Salter.
'My head,' said Rocky.
'Can you move your hands?' asked Fireman Salter.
'I can move one of them,' said Rocky.
'Then reach up and take the helmet off.' he said.
It took Rocky a while but at last the helmet came off.
The firemen started to pull again and this time
Rocky moved.
Rocky was lifted clear and there was a big cheer at
the top of the hole.
But the helmet and a big pile of wet mud came falling
down on me.

I could hear them talking.
'You were very brave,' said Rocky's Mum.
'Yes,' said Rocky, 'but I didn't get him out. Max is still down there.'
'But now we can see him,' said Fireman Salter.
Rocky was surprised.
It was true.
The camera on the helmet gave the firemen a good picture of me down in the hole.
Rocky must have been pleased to see me again.

'But I'm afraid things don't look good,' said
Fireman Salter.
'Max is hurt. He can't stand up and the mud is
starting to fall in on him.'
'What can we do?' asked Rocky.
Then I heard Fred.
He wanted to help.
'Can't we dig another hole next to this one and
tunnel through to Max?'
'No,' said Fireman Salter. 'That would take too long.
We don't have much time. We must work quickly.'

Chapter 4 Water wings

The next idea to get me out was a very simple one.
They let down a basket on a wire.
If I could just get into the basket they were going to
pull me up.
But now they could see on the TV screen that I
couldn't move.
My leg was hurt too badly.
I just couldn't get into that basket.
I tried hard but the mud was still falling on me.
It was getting so heavy.
I could just about keep my head above it and
get my breath.

I could tell everyone at the top of the hole was
getting very worried.
I could hear them talking.
There was a man from the RSPCA, and a
reporter from the newspaper.
They wanted to know what Fireman Salter was
going to do next.
'The side of the tunnel is falling in,' he said.
How were they going to get me out?

Then Rocky had an idea.
He went over to talk to Fireman Salter.
At first Fireman Salter didn't think that Rocky's idea would work.
But they were running out of time so he said, 'Let's try it.'
Rocky rushed back home.
While he was gone Fireman Salter told his men what they were going to do next.
They sounded surprised.
When Rocky returned he had his water wings with him.
His Mum bought them for him when he was trying to learn to swim.
'What are you going to do with those?' she asked.
'Wait and see!' said Rocky, who didn't have
time to stop.
Fireman Salter and Rocky stood together at the
top of the hole.
Rocky blew air into the water wings.
Fireman Salter told everyone to be quiet.
Everyone watched quietly.
What was going to happen next?
Rocky suddenly called down to me.
'Hello, Max. Can you hear me?'
I gave a small woof.

'Good boy,' he said. 'I'm going to send down some water wings on a wire. I'm going to try and get them on your front legs. Then we are going to fill the hole with water. You will come up as the water comes up. Do you understand, boy?'

Then some water wings came down the hole on a wire.

They landed too far away from me but Fireman Salter did a very clever thing.

By watching the small TV he was able to move them nearer and nearer.

He tried again and again to get the water wings near to me.

At last he did it!

I was able to push my front legs through the hole.

'Well done, Max!' shouted Rocky.

'You are a clever dog. You did understand!'

Of course I understood.

I'm not stupid, you know!

I heard the fire engine pumps start up.
Soon the water started to splash down into the tunnel.
It was cold, very cold.
But would it work?
I might drown, or I might swim.
The water was nearly up to my nose and
I was really scared.
Then slowly I felt myself lifting up with the water.
It was starting to work.
But it was still a long way up to the top.

The danger wasn't over.
As the water rose up the mud came down hard and fast.
A great pile of mud was falling down on me.
It splashed all around me.
I tried to hold on to the water wings as tightly as I could.

27

Chapter 5 A special dog!

At last I could see the top of the hole.

The light was so bright it was difficult to see who was out there.

I could hear everyone getting excited as I got near the top.

At last I felt hands pulling me out of the water.

It was Fireman Salter.

'Come on boy, you're safe now,' he said.

Everyone shouted and cheered.

Someone put warm clothes around me.

It was Rocky's Mum.

Rocky was there with a big smile on his face.

The next few days were strange.
The vet at the Animal Hospital put this
hard stuff on my leg.
I could walk a little bit but I got tired very quickly.
Everyone was great to me.
I knew I was getting better.

'Max, you're a very special dog,' said Rocky.
I had always thought I was special.
Now I knew I was, because I had my picture in the
newspaper!

I still keep Rocky's water wings in my basket by the door.
You never know when we might need them again.
Every day something new happens in
Wellington Square.
I wonder what will happen today?